TALES OF TI

Tales of the Banshee

Selected and introduced by

PATRICK F. BYRNE

THE MERCIER PRESS

The Mercier Press Limited
4 Bridge Street, Cork
24 Lower Abbey Street, Dublin 1

This edition 1991

British Library Cataloguing in Publication Data
Tales of the Banshee
1. Banshees
I. Byrne, Patrick F.
398'.45 GR153.5

ISBN 0 85342 972 3

For my grandchildren, Nicola and Luke,
hoping it may introduce them to
the magic of Irish folklore.

Printed in Ireland by Colour Books Ltd,. Dublin

Contents

Acknowledgements

The first seven stories appeared in various Irish periodicals during the latter part of the nineteenth century. For permission to quote material from the *Evening Herald* Ghosts Column, I must thank the paper's Editor, Mr Michael Brophy and Independent Newspapers Ltd., the Mercier Press for extracts from two books published by them, and Pádraig Ó Héalaí, Editor of *Béaloideas*. Last, but not least, I must record how much I was indebted to Patricia Lysaght's scholarly work, *The Banshee*, which proved to be an invaluable source book.

Introduction

'Not for base-born higgling Saxon trucksters, waileth our banshee,' wrote James Clarence Mangan in his translation of Piaras Feiriteir's 'Lament for the death of Sir Maurice Fitzgerald, Knight of Kerry' who was killed in a battle in Flanders in 1642. He was a descendant of a Norman family who became 'more Irish than the Irish themselves', and therefore qualified for the same privileges as those of ancient native lineage. In the poem the phantom mourners are described as 'Mogeeley's phantom women'.

The origin of the Banshee is lost in the mists of antiquity. There is obviously a connection with the *sidhe bhean* (fairy woman) mentioned in the old sagas. Such a one was Niamh of the Golden Hair who came from Tír-na-nÓg (the land of youth), the Celtic Heaven, and carried Oisín back there on a white horse. In 'The White Goddess' Robert Graves connects the Banshee with the burial mound at Newgrange, a 'Woman of the Hill', priestess of the great dead – 'she wails in prophetic anticipation whenever anyone of royal blood is about to die.'

Perhaps it was years of persecution by Danes and

English that turned the Banshee into a withered screeching hag, combing her tousled hair with a broken comb. It was by telling stories of seeing and hearing such a creature that my mother and grandmother frightened me at night at the fireside in the heart of the Liberties in Dublin many years ago. It always happened when an old neighbour lay dying.

In some parts of the country she is known as the *bean chaointe* (keening woman) and in other places, particularly in Wexford as the badhbh, described in Dinneen's dictionary as 'a female fairy or phantom said to be attached to certain families, appearing as a scald-crow or roystoncrow'. The bird connection predominates in the old sagas, one landing on Cuchulainn's shoulder as he lay dying, tied to the stone pillar.

The O'Neills and the Banshee were inseparably connected, and for years in the Co. Antrim area around Shane's Castle to hear the Banshee's cry was considered an ill-omen. If a fisherman heard her it was a sure sign of a great storm on the lake and he would not go out in his boat for it was said that Lough Neagh claimed five lives every year. For a pair of lovers to hear the cry when strolling in the moonlight it was a sure sign that their wooing would soon end. For a farmer it meant his crops would fail or his cattle die, and the poor people counted it as a sign of approaching famine, pestilence and war. The oldest inhabitant would tell about the room that was set apart in the castle for the Banshee, and if its bed was not made, and a comb and water not left for its use, there was no sleep for the inmates of the castle that night.

As well as the O'Neills – the O'Briens, the O'Connors, the O'Donnells, the O'Gradys, the Kavanaghs, and other septs have each had their Banshee. She was supposed to come expressly for the purpose of forewarning death, which she did by melancholy wailings, appearing in the form of a young and beautiful woman, arrayed in white, but more frequently as a frightful hag, and often as a mere 'voice' as invisible and elusive as an echo. Night was the time generally chosen by the Banshee for her visits, as an ancient bard has written:

The Banshee mournful wails
In the midst of the silent, lonely night.
Plaintive she sings the song of death

But she has also been heard at noon 'when mid-day is silent around', and when the 'voices' of several sing together coming to the ear like:

Aery tongues, that syllable men's names,
On sand, and shore, and desert wilderness.

On these occasions they were not always considered an omen of evil, for we find the poet Oisín in an old Irish poem, enumerating among the sounds that Fionn Mac Cumhaill delighted to hear – 'the slow chilling sounds' of these aerial voices.

The appearance of the Banshee in the morning is rare: this appearance is alluded to in a very old Irish poem; the following is a translation of a passage –

> Hast thou heard the Banshee at morn; passing by the silent lake, or walking the fields by the orchard. Alas! that I do not rather behold white garlands in the hall of thy fathers!

In her 'Memoirs' published in 1830, Lady Fanshawe tells of how she went with her husband on a visit to Lady Honoria O'Brien in her mansion in Co. Clare, where they stayed three nights. 'On the first of these nights,' she wrote, 'I received a great surprise in my chamber, when about one o'clock, I heard a voice that awakened me.

'I drew the curtain, and, in the casement of the window, I saw by the light of the moon a woman outside leaning in. She had red hair and a pale and ghastly complexion. She spoke loud, and in a tone I had never heard, thrice, "A Horse!" and then with a sigh, more like the wind than breath, she vanished, and to me her body looked more like a thick cloud than substance. I was so much frightened that my hair stood on end, and my night clothes fell off. I pulled and pinched my husband, who never awoke during the incident, but was much surprised to see my fright, and more so when I related the story, and showed him the window open.

'In the morning the lady of the house came to see us, saying she had not been in bed all night because a cousin of hers named O'Brien, whose ancestors had owned the house, had died during the night, and she had been sitting in his room until the end came at 2 a.m. She added – "I hope you have had no disturbance, for it's a custom of this place, that when any member of the famiy is dying, the shape of a woman appears in the window. This woman was many years ago seduced by the owner of this place, who murdered her in his garden, and flung her into the river under the window. But truly I thought not of it when I lodged you here, it being the best room in the house."

'We made but little reply to her speech, but decided to go as soon as we could.'

Lady Fanshawe was renowned for having a sound, clear and unexcitable head, and if a trick was being played on her, she would have seen through it.

The late Miss Annie M. P. Smithson, the popular Irish novelist, in her autobiography, *Myself and Others* tells of an experience she had while nursing in Co. Clare in the early years of the century. One night, sharing a room with another nurse, they were awakened by a most awful sound –

> It was like the long drawn-out wailing of a soul in torment. The Banshee, I thought, and began to feel that horrid prickling of the scalp which we describe by saying that 'our hair rose'. On and on it went wailing back and forth among the rocks in a wild bit of woodland, just across the road from our cottage. A lost soul

in torment – the cry of one lost forever – forever wandering in the outer darkness. Near morning the wailing stopped, and we fell asleep.

Later that day one of my patients said to me: 'So the Banshee was on the rocks last night – were ye frightened?' I heard nothing about any death in the area, but the wail will never be forgotten.

Lady Wilde spoke of the Banshee as 'the spirit of death – the most weird and awful of all the fairy powers', and added 'but only certain families of ancient lineage or persons gifted with music and song are attended by this spirit.'

The Legend of Dunluce

On the northern coast of Antrim, about midway between Portrush and the Giant's Causeway, perched on a rock, almost separated from the mainland by a precipitous chasm, stand the ruins of the castle of Dunluce. In the fifteenth century, Maeve, the only daughter of the Lord of Dunluce, a girl of seventeen, lived with her father in the fortress. Gentle and charitable, she rose at dawn, and spent her day helping the poor dependants who lived on the estate. During one of her walks she met a handsome cavalier, and thereafter encountered him many times, falling in love with him. Where he came from she did not know, but eventually the news of their meetings reached the ears of her father, MacQuillian, who had plans to wed her to the son of a rich and powerful neighbour.

But the girl decided she would rather die than marry someone she did not love, so she began to knit a shroud. One day her father found her at work on it and asked, 'Is this your bridal dress?'

'No father,' she replied, 'it is my shroud.'

'A shroud! We shall see to that.'

'Yes father, you shall see it.'

The enraged father then decided to lock her up in one of the towers, where she was obliged to make her own bed and sweep her room. One day her father came to the door and said – 'Only promise to wed the noble chief I have selected for you, and you shall have your freedom.' She didn't answer. 'What have you decided?' he shouted.

'To sweep my room.'

'For how long?'

'Forever.'

'Are you still making your shroud?'

'It's finished. You shall see it.'

Seeing that nothing would change her mind, the Lord began to feel remorse. Either he must yield, or she must die. He found out who the mysterious lover was. His name was Reginald, a brave youth, of noble birth and wealthy. He made a decision – he would not yield, but would still save his child.

One day, as a storm raged outside and the thunder pealed, Maeve was weeping in her turret. That morning her father had left the castle with an escort of soldiers and was not due to return for some days. To her surprise she heard the key turning in the lock, and the door opened. It was one of her father's servants.

'You shall be saved, he awaits you,' said the man. 'Follow me.'

He led her to the cavern below the fort where her

lover greeted her. He said that having heard her father was leaving he had bribed the servant who had freed her. She got into the small boat her lover had waiting, and the frail craft set out on the stormy sea.

From a window her father watched; the escape had been part of a plan he concocted, pretending to leave, but secretly re-entering the castle. The servant had been his accomplice. MacQuillian rejoiced to have discovered the means of restoring life and happiness to his daughter, without in any way sacrificing his pride.

His eyes were on the little boat as it made its way through the raging sea. 'Alas,' he said, 'that I should be obliged to see my daughter driven from home, and myself the cause of it. They think of nothing at the moment but their love. It matters not, I have saved her.'

But just as he spoke he saw the boat rise up on top of a large wave and suddenly disappear. He rushed out and called to his men to try and save her, but it was too late. She had disappeared for ever.

For weeks, the father, mad with grief, walked along the shore calling on his daughter. One day, passing under the tower where she had shed so many tears, he looked up. A strange vision! Maeve was at the bars of the window clad in her shroud with her broom in her hand. Bereft of reason, her father cried – 'For how long?'

'For ever' came the reply, and the figure showed him her shroud saying, 'It is finished as you see.'

She became the Banshee of the family, but since the family died out she appears no longer. But they say that one can still hear her broom sweeping on a quiet, calm day.

In the Year of the French

The village of Glanmore in Co. Mayo stands on the rocky shore of a small, deep and transparent lake. On one shore a steep hill rises and it is covered with large rocks, rising ridge-like over each other. Between the rocks, bush, briar and shrub tangle so closely, that a fox or wild cat could scarcely force a passage through. Down the centre of the hill a torrent runs its course on the way to feed a lake with the unceasing flow of its waters. The only bridge across the torrent is the craggy edge of an immense rock, some sixty feet above. Beneath one of the biggest of the isolated rocks there is a large cave which tradition records was used as a hiding place by the Danes in olden times. It became, after the defeat of the French and insurgents at Ballinamuck the asylum of James Stanford, a bold and daring insurgent captain.

A harvest moon was rising in a beautiful sky of light, fleecy clouds, veined with streaks of blue, as he stood watching a form that was climbing towards him by a path where a mountain goat would hardly find a footing. The moon brightened as he bounded forward to assist the girl who had risked life and limb to visit him. She was muffled in a cloak and bonnet, and carried a small parcel and some food. Greeting her he said, 'Jane, my love, this is the last time you will have to venture here; by this hour tomorrow night we will be far away from this place and from danger.'

She answered by pressing his hand, and he saw by the moonlight a tear in her eye; he kissed it off, and they were soon seated in the cavern.

Jane Hamilton was considered to be one of the prettiest maidens in the barony of Glanmore, and although differing in religion from her neighbours, she was as well beloved by them as if she were of their kith and kin. Her father, Aaron Hamilton, had come from 'the Black North' to settle in the area. He had obtained a farm at a trifling rent from the local landlord, and had built it into the most thriving one on the estate. He was also reported to have made a little on the side from smuggled contraband such as brandy and tobacco. He had also carefully avoided becoming involved in the events which led to the recent insurrection.

To his daughter he was always a tender and affectionate parent especially since the death of his wife three years before. She was entrusted with every key in the house. For her his garden smiled, his ground was improved, and the produce of his early and late work hoarded. Without his knowledge, Jane managed to spend some time at most of the weddings, christenings, wakes and merry-makings in the village. It was at one of these festive occasions that she met James Stanford. The evening before he set out to join the invaders, she offered to foresake her home, her father and even her religion, and link herself to him for ever, if he would renounce his mad enterprise. Now he was a proscribed outlaw with a price on his head, hiding in a wild place, but she still loved him.

It was a week since Stanford's escape from the battlefield, during which period Jane had climbed nightly to the cavern to supply him with provisions, as he dared not venture to Glanmore, where the King's troops had been in pursuit of him and others. This time she had left her father's house for good, for they planned to escape to America in a vessel that lay along the coast nearby. After she had dyed her lover's face a deep tawny hue and transformed his fair curly hair to black, they carefully started their descent towards the sea. When a noise, as of distant voices behind, caught the keen ears of Jane, she turned and saw glittering in the moonbeams, the arms and dress of soldiers, who were winding around and ascending the hill. The girl screamed and said 'God help us, James. They are after us, they were at our house when I was leaving,' and she sank in a faint at his feet.

He turned and looked at the soldiers advancing, and they saw him. It was a moment of terror and indecision. His life was on a line. But could he leave behind the woman who had left all for him? Suddenly the moon disappeared behind a veil of clouds. Immediately he snatched Jane up in his arms, and bounding fearlessly over crag and chasm, was lost to the sight of his pursuers before the next ray broke through. The soldiers had now reached the edge of the torrent, and it took them a while to reach the rock bridge. As they approached a female figure in white appeared, moving from the far side of the hill and having seated herself on one of the ledges of rocks that formed the shore, began to wash something in the lake, while, in a wild and melancholy voice, she began to sing an ancient Irish air.

After a while she arose, and began slowly to ascend the hill, still singing, and now and again clapping between her hands what she had been washing. As she went up her voice rose wildly, and then sank into mournful cadences which were echoed by the thousand voices of the rocks. The group of soldiers watched, fear mingling with their astonishment.

'It must be the Banshee,' whispered one in terror.

'A Banshee! What's that?'

'A woman spirit that comes to ancient families to warn of a death coming to one of them,' replied the first.

'But there's no ancient family on top of that hill.'

'Who can tell where she may be goin' to? Sometimes she's to be seen at the stream washing the winding sheet; other times she comes around the house, combing her hair, and always singing dismally as she is now.'

'It's all a rebel's trick,' said the doubting soldier. 'Banshee or devil, I'll take a shot at her,' and he presented his musket and fired. The figure in the distance fell to the ground. In his eagerness to reach his target, the soldier lost his footing on one of the rocks, and fell down headlong to disappear in the murky waters below.

His comrades continued on more carefully, and reached the spot where the figure lay. It was not a supernatural being, but a poor mortal female, covered in blood and on the point of death. She had a sheet wound around her head and body, and even in her death throes she still had clasped to her what she had been washing – a man's waistcoat as bloodstained as her own garments. It was afterwards they found out who the hapless victim was.

Sally Ryan and Myles Staunton had courted for a year and were to be married the day the French landed at Killala. But Myles joined the insurgents and the wedding was deferred, and they did not meet again until after the disastrous defeat at Ballinamuck, in which he was badly wounded. He managed to reach Sally's cottage, but died shortly afterwards. The grief-stricken woman lost her reason, and every day brought his blood-stained waistcoat to the lake to try and wash away the stains.

The soldiers carried her body back to her parents' cottage in Glanmore. They had decided, after the loss of their comrade to abandon the chase after the wanted man.

Stanford and Jane had made good time, and long before morning broke had reached the boat. It was not long before they were safely in a land where neither a father's wrath nor a savage soldiery could reach them.

A Love Story

The only daughter of parents of sufficient distinction in the estimation of the people to have an attendant spirit, was loved by and returned the attachment of a youth, her inferior both in birth and fortune. She was one of those quickly susceptible and gently yielding creatures, who, although gifted with warm affection, have probably not the strength to sustain it through grief and through danger, through sorrow and shame.

While he was by her side, she felt as though she could have died sooner than have forgotten him. They used to meet stealthily in the moonlight and before the lark had poised her dewy wings in the morning sun. They exchanged vows of everlasting constancy believing all they uttered to be the pure and unalterable truth. The girl at this time was barely seventeen, but the young man was twenty-four. Irishmen have the reputation of being quick at loving and quick at forgetting; it was not so with him. His nature was firm and fervent; he would have loved her had she been the poorest girl who watched the sheep upon his native mountain.

'I will not wed you against your father's will,' he said, 'but I will gain a name and come back to you with fame and honour – I will do this, by God's grace; I will be as faithful as the stars which are brightly shining on us now, if you will promise here and now by my side to wait, free from other love, until I return.'

The girl promised as he desired, placing her finger against his finger. She slipped on to his finger a ring esteemed by her family as one of rare value, making him in return promise that if he died or became indifferent to her, or married another, he should return the ring to her. He readily agreed to do this, and the lovers parted. Mary exclaimed in the wild anguish of her first sorrow, 'Surely, surely, if he had loved me as I love him, he would never have proposed this parting. Well, well, he knew I would have flown with him to the world's end.' And he *did* know it; but her weak nature was unable to appreciate the virtue of the sacrifice he made by tearing himself from the only thing he valued on earth; no taint of selfishness sullied the brightness of his devotion. He would not submit her to the pangs of self-reproach for having deserted her aged parents if they eloped.

The years rolled on. Six or seven years passed away and no tidings arrived of the absent lover. As they went by, the first suspicion that had disturbed her mind gained strength – 'if he had loved me as I loved him, he would never have proposed this parting.' It might be that she used this feeling as an excuse for the fickleness of her own heart as the arguments and entreaties of her family induced her, at length, to listen to the addresses of a wealthy suitor, and after some reluctance, to agree to marry him.

It is only fair to say that Mary had waited, and waited, and waited with the sickness of a sorrowing heart for the return of her lover. Many were ready and willing to work upon her fears and stories came from 'foreign parts' whispering that he was untrue to the vows of his early love.

'And so,' said one of the gossiping old neighbours to another, 'and so Mary O'Neill after all is going to marry the hardest man in the country!'

'Oh, sure,' was the reply, 'if he's hard he's high; and set one against the other, she'll be well off. She's neither as young nor as pretty as she was seven years ago, when he that's over the seas used to meet her on the up-hill side, or by the silent rock, or under the rowan tree. Ah! if trees and rocks could speak, what a deal they'd have to tell of the falsity of man and the folly of women!'

'There's no falsity there, unless you call Mary's change falsity,' replied the old woman, 'but the Lord only knows how it'll end – the Lord above, and one other.'

'What!' exclaimed the first speaker, in a half-whisper. 'You do not mean that. Have you heard anything, Nelly, dear?'

The two drew more closely together. 'You know the family has a follower, dear. They're of the real old sort; and that's never forgot. The Banshee that does be after them is not as strong as she used to be long, long ago, though she is strong enough to give the death warning. It's as good as seven years since Miss Mary's first sweetheart met her for the last time, and I was coming up the glen the same night from old Mary Roon's wake, and I came upon them unawares. I kept still so as not to disturb them, for she was crying like a new-born baby that had lost its mother and his words without tears would pierce through stone walls. Well I saw them put finger to finger, and slip on a ring. As they did, and as sure as there's but one star of the thousands looking at us now, the cry came through the air soft and sorrowful. Not the wail for present death, but what would end that way.'

'Maybe,' suggested her companion, 'it was for him!'

'For him,' repeated the other in a tone of deep indignation. 'Why, then, I'm ashamed of your ignorance, you poor creature! Is it doting you are, woman alive? What right would the likes of him have to the cry of a Banshee?'

The woman added that on the evening Mr and Mrs O'Neill and the priest, and the 'hard man' persuaded Miss Mary to pledge a troth she had no right to pledge – the cry was heard more than once about the place, sharper and clearer than before. Who heard it as well she could not tell. She only knew she heard it, and would swear she did to her dying day.

'And it was nearer, you say?'

'Nearer and sharper – too near, as some will find. It can't be for her mother, and if it was for her father, I can't see the sense of its holding on when it's she that's acting. The first time I heard it, it wound through the air like a misty cloud creeping up a mountain – it was a soft, sorrowful wail! The second time it was bitter and angry.'

'And the third time, Nelly?'

'I've not heard it the third time – yet,' she answered solemnly, 'and I don't want to. The fine old families are fading out of the country entirely – going away like chaff – and such spirits will have no call to the new people. My father (rest his soul!) used to say that from what he knew, he was sure they would soon quit the country. Maybe so, but anyhow, we'll be lonesome when they go, for it's hard wanting the knowledge that we're cared for by something besides bare flesh and blood.'

'And when will the wedding be, Nelly? Sure a wedding's a godsend these hard times. It's hard if we don't get full and plenty at the wedding of the heiress!'

'Ah!' said the other, 'tomorrow week, and there'll be heaps of quality in it, besides lashings of people from far and near, and all the ancient customs kept up! And so it'll be worth going to these hard times.'

Although the bride could not be said to give any symptoms of repenting her new betrothment, she seemingly took little interest in the proceedings. Perhaps she had been taunted with the reproach of old-maidenhood – and led to believe it would be wrong for the last of her line to go down unwed to the grave. The fact that she received no tidings of her former lover sealed her destiny,

It was not the custom at the time for the bride and bridegroom to absent themselves immediately after the marriage, and the wedding was solemnised in the usual old Irish fashion. The bride remained to do the honours and welcome the guests. As was also the practice at that time the window curtains were allowed to remain undrawn, so that the crowd outside could feast their eyes on the crowd within, whose movements they observed and commented on. When anything particularly pleased them, they gave a loud 'hurrah'.

The two women, whose observations have been recorded, were also there with their withered faces pressed against the glass to observe what was going on. Occasionally they abused those who pressed too closely on them from behind and vented their spleen in bitter words and curses. Suddenly, Nelly, whose reputation for foreknowledge had gained her anything but a pleasant popularity, crushed her bony fingers around her companion's arm – 'whisht, did you hear nothing?'

'Nothing, dear, but the boys cheering for the wedding.'

'You're a deaf fool!' said Nelly, throwing her arms around excitedly.

The bride had risen to meet a strange guest who, unknown and unannounced, had entered the large parlour where the feast was gong on. Without returning her salutation he asked for a drink. She gave him a goblet of wine. He refused to touch it and asked her to change it for water, which, he declared was his only beverage. She then presented him with the water, which he drank. But she saw that as he returned the glass he had dropped something into it. Before she could discover what it was he disappeared amidst the crowd. Looking into the goblet she recognised her own ring – the very one she had given to her betrothed at their parting. Now she knew who the stranger was. She was deeply moved, but said nothing as the wedding-feast continued.

An hour later a woman rushed into the house to look for the priest who was one of the guests. She said a stranger had asked for shelter beneath her roof, and she feared, had dropped dead at her fireside. The truth now dawned on the bride. He did, indeed, truly love her. Forgetting her ill-advised marriage, and clinging to the hope that he was still alive, she rushed out and ran to the woman's house. As she crossed the threshold of the cottage door a fierce and mighty wind swept around the house although the night was calm and mild. Everyone paused and trembled at the cry – the well-known wail of the Banshee, so full, and then so agonising in its dying fall.

The bride flew on, she was the only one of the terror-stricken revellers who did not pause or pray. She went into the cottage, and flung herself on her knees beside him – pressed her hand on his heart – there was no sign of life. She called him by his name – there was no reply. Stooping down, she kissed his cold lips. She knew then that he was dead. In the presence of her kinfolk and her husband who had followed her she tore the silver ribbon from her hair, and burst forth into a wild death-cry – a mournful keen over the dead body of her lover. As the cries ended, she fell dead on her beloved's body.

They were laid to rest side by side. A few weeks after the tragedy the Banshee cried again. This time it was for the father of Mary O'Neill – the last of his line.

In that part of the country two trees are still shown as heading the grave of those who 'in death were not divided'.

A County Cork Tragedy

I was the youngest of three sisters left orphans by the death of our dear mother when I was only thirteen years old. Mary, next to me was fifteen at the time, Julia, the eldest was seventeen. Our father had been killed by an accident in the hunting field about three years before. We had only one brother, Henry, but he turned out 'wild', as the expression goes, disgraced himself long before father died, and left for Australia. We never heard from him, and his name was never mentioned in the household.

When mother died we three sisters left Whitefort Castle in Co. Cork, where we had spent many happy years and went to live with Uncle Philip at Millford House, about five miles distant. Uncle had managed our estate after father's death and he and his wife received us with great kindness. They did everything in their power to comfort us in our sad affliction. We were as happy as we could be under the circumstances.

Millford House, one of the finest mansions in the south of Ireland, was charmingly situated on the side of a slightly rising hill. It had large gardens and neatly-kept walks which led down to the margin of an artificial lake. Out of this lake a little river flowed, spanned at each end by two small bridges, and away in the background was a thickly-planted wood.

Meanwhile, our ancestral home, Whitefort Castle had been rented to a London gentleman, who liked the locality, and was delighted to find a secluded, rural retreat away from the bustle of city life. After we had been in Millford for about four years an event occurred which changed the whole pattern of my girlish days.

Among the tutors who came to give lessons to me and my sisters was a man of about thirty-five, quiet and reserved in manner; graceful and dignified in appearance. He was the youngest son of a gentleman well known in sporting circles who was obliged to mortgage his estate to pay his gaming debts. He was forced to give lessons on the violin, an instrument of which he was the perfect master. He held us spellbound and accompanied by Mary on the piano, he played selections from Chopin, Mendelssohn, or Mozart.

It is not surprising that I fell in love with George Freeman from the first moment I saw him, but I kept this to myself, and our conversation mainly concerned the lessons I was having.

My eldest sister, Julia, had always been impetuous and headstrong and cared little for society, preferring the solitude of her room and reading books. She had been subject from an early age to fits of somnambulism, which caused us great concern, for frequently she was rescued from perilous positions during her sleep-walking, and on such occasions our main concern was to make sure she didn't get outside the house.

She was about twenty-one at this time, when I suddenly realised that she was becoming strongly attached to the young violinist. There had never been much sympathy between us and when I saw her gazing lovingly at him a feeling akin to jealousy and hatred entered my heart. I tried to overcome the feeling but without success.

George Freeman continued to visit the house daily to give us our lessons. Mary, who shared a bedroom with Julia, because of her sleep-walking, had gone to visit friends in London. The relationship between Julia and myself prevented me from offering to take Mary's place at night, for which I many times afterwards reproached myself.

One day around this time when I was reading in a little summer house in one of the gardens, Betty, our old nurse, who had looked after us since we were born, came to me in great agitation. 'I want to tell you about a thing that's troubling me,' she said, 'I couldn't keep it to myself any longer, and as it concerns you I thought I'd tell you. You know, or you may have heard that the Banshee follows your family. We heard her in the kitchen in the castle when your poor mother died, and for three nights before the master, God rest him, passed away, we heard the wailing all around the castle.

'Well, my darling, I don't want to frighten you, but the night before last, just as I was going to bed, as the big clock in the stable yard beyond was striking twelve, clear out of the still air of the night, I heard again the dismal, mournful cry of the Banshee. I hope, Miss Angela, that it doesn't portend that death or sorrow is coming to you or your sisters – who knows but it may mean that poor Master Harry is dead away out in foreign parts?'

Although I tried to make light of what Betty had said, and even though I was not by any means superstitious, I couldn't avoid feeling a dread of some calamity happening. I had heard the servants at Whiteford from time to time talk of the Banshee and her visits to the neighbourhood of our home, and I had always laughed at them treating their talk as fanciful creations.

In vain I tried to persuade Betty that it was a human voice she heard and that the Banshee's cry only existed in her imagination, but all to no purpose. That night, just before retiring, I noted that Julia was in her usual good spirits as I kissed her goodnight. Only that day a letter had arrived from Mary, saying she was enjoying her visit, but despite all this the feeling of gloom was still with me as I went to bed. I couldn't sleep for a long while and then I sank into an uneasy slumber. I was awakened as the clock struck one. Something made me get up and look out of the window. A beautiful moon shone and was reflected in the calm water of the lake.

As I gazed out I suddenly became aware that a female figure, clad in white, was walking along the edge of the lake, close to one of the rustic bridges. She reached it, and then stood midway upon it. Terror struck me as I realised it could be Julia in one of her sleep-walking fits, and should she miss her footing, she would plunge into the waters of the lake.

My first reaction was to rush to her room and to my horror the bed was empty! Quickly putting on a dress and a large shawl I ran down to the front door, opened it, and sped across the terrace down to the garden. In a few minutes I reached the pond but looked in vain for my sister. At this moment a dense black cloud moved across the moon, plunging the surroundings into darkness. However, I managed to find my way to the bridge, and as I reached it the moon came out again. I looked down, and in the water beneath me I saw my sister Julia lying on her back, and supported under the surface by the thick weeds, with her beautiful tresses floating around her placidly-smiling lovely face.

All at once the nurse's story of the Banshee's warning came into my mind. I gave a loud cry and fainted by the lakeside. How long I lay there I couldn't tell, but on opening my eyes I saw standing over me the tall form of George Freeman. Shivering in my light clothing, he carried me back to the house. Meanwhile, the servants were aroused and my sister's body was raised from its watery resting-place and brought home.

Because of shock and exposure I caught a fever and lay for days hovering between life and death. George Freeman came to the house to inquire as to how I was every day. He was greeted by Mary, who had, of course, returned home. I recovered at last and learned from George the story of his appearance at the scene of my sister's death.

That night, he said, he couldn't sleep, and having been in bed for some time got up and went out. He strolled away from the village where he lodged, and enjoying the beauty of the moonlight scene, made his way into the demesne of Millford House. As he approached the lake, he heard a piercing cry – my shriek of anguish – coming from the other side. Rushing around to the spot he came to my unconscious body and saw Julia lying in the water.

A year or so passed after the events just related and I was sitting reading in the drawing-room at Millford, with Mary sitting opposite me, when suddenly she said, 'Angela, do you hear that cry? That mournful, dismal, wailing cry?' I had heard nothing and told her so. Mary fell back into her chair, but although both of us said nothing more we were full of foreboding.

A few minutes later, a loud knock was heard on the hall door. A servant came up to say that a messenger with a trap was waiting outside to take Mary and myself to Whitefort, at the desire of Mr Grey, the gentleman from London, who lived there. This puzzled us as he was a quiet, retiring man, and we had never seen him over the years. Having got ready, we seated ourselves in the carriage, and arrived at the castle at about eleven o'clock.

Imagine our surprise on being led to a bedroom upstairs to find that the gentleman who lay on the bed, with a doctor standing by him, and a lawyer writing at a side table, was no other than our long-lost brother, Henry. Yes, much changed by sickness, and known to the people around him as 'Mr Grey'. He was dying, but in his last breath told us how he had been attracted back to the old castle, but because of his mis-spent youth, had been afraid to let us know who he was. Later we heard that his wealth – the accumulation of years of toil – had been divided in his will between Mary and me.

Thus, it would seem, for a second time in my experience, the dreaded warning of the Banshee was fulfilled. I have little more to tell. It was not fated that I should marry George Freeman, any more than my sister, Julia, who was so suddenly snatched away from us. Within a year after Henry's death George proposed to, and was accepted by, Mary. After their marriage they went to live in the old family residence of Whitefort where they lived for many happy years. George never knew the secret of my love for him.

I continued to live with my uncle who had no children of his own, paying occasional visits to the castle. I never married, and now at sixty years of age one of my great pleasures is to admire the grace and beauty of my grand-nephews and nieces, the charming children of the eldest son of George Freeman, who having succeeded a few years before his death to his father's estate and title, was known as Lord Fremont of Whitefort.

The Banshee's Revenge upon the Fitzpatricks

On the right-hand side of the little by-road, which leads the traveller from the famous bog of Monela to the northern range of the Slievebloom Mountains, stood the uninhabited mansion of a gentleman named Fitzpatrick, who had the reputation of being an absentee landlord. The Fitzpatricks of Ossory and the Ormonds of Kilkenny were deadly foes for centuries. More than one of the illustrious house of Butler were prisoners of their implacable enemies, and in the reign of Charles I, the celebrated Duke of Ormond completely destroyed the power of the Fitzpatricks and annexed Durrow, their patrimony, to his own possessions, since which time that district forms part of the county of Kilkenny.

Some time previous to this period, one of the Butlers over-ran Lower Ossory, and as usual, having slaughtered most of its inhabitants, the heir of the house of Fitzpatrick found refuge in the castle of O'More, the chieftain of Laois. He was regarded as an honoured guest, and treated as one of the family, so much so that O'More took no precaution to prevent any improper intimacy between Fitzpatrick and his only daughter, a lady 'who possessed to any eminent degree all those charms which added to the attractions of youth and beauty'.

The consequence of parental neglect on this occasion proved fatal, and, as the story goes, continued to affect the happiness of the descendants of one of the party. The chieftain's lovely daughter naturally attracted the attentions of her father's guest, who was about her own age, and as no restraint was placed upon their meetings, they felt natural happiness in each other's company.

They were indiscreet, and to their horror discovered that a knowledge of their conduct must soon take place. They knew the wrath of O'More would be fierce, and he would be unlikely to pardon them, and that both their lives would be forfeit, unless they could make their escape. Under these circumstances they decided to fly from Laois, and arranged to meet one evening at a lonely well to arrange for their departure. The lady was there at the appointed time, but when her lover arrived, while in the act of caressing her, he plunged a dagger into her heart. As she fell dead, her blood tinged the water in the spring, and Fitzpatrick returned undiscovered to the castle. The chieftain lamented the fate of his child, but never suspected his guest. The heir of Ossory for a time encountered no reproof but that of his own guilty conscience.

Shortly afterwards Fitzpatrick was restored by O'More to his possessions in Ossory, where he married and had several children. The memory of the lovely victim had nearly been forgotten until one night when Fitzpatrick and his followers, during a tribal war, were encamped not far from the fatal spot where he had committed the murder, the awful piercing cry of the Banshee was heard coming from the well. The guilty chieftain was startled, but, as if impelled by some supernatural power, walked towards the spring, and distinctly saw the victim of his treachery, in her ordinary dress of white, sitting beneath the tree that shaded the well, and wringing her hands as if in an agony of grief. As he gazed on her, she arose, redoubled her cries and moved towards him. Overcome by fear, he sank to his knees and shouted – 'Pardon, oh! pardon your murderer!' The apparition gave a hoarse scream, and vanished like the shadow of morning down the valley still keeping up the cry of the Banshee.

The cry had scarcely ceased when the sentinel gave the alarm of a sudden attack and the O'Mores in an instant were in the camp of the Fitzpatricks. The battle was long and bloody; but before the morning sun arose the heroes of Laois prevailed, and the chief of Ossory fell beneath the weapon of his old protector's son, confessing before he died, that his was the fatal hand by which the sister of the conqueror was slain.

After this the cry of the Banshee was regularly heard at the fatal well before the death of any of the descendants of Fitzpatrick, and in time it became so notorious that the spring became known as the 'Banshee's Well'. No matter whether a Fitzpatrick died in war or peace, at home or abroad, the cry that foretold the sad event was to be heard where the apparition first appeared. Local tradition had it that the Banshee was the ghost of the murdered lady, announcing retribution for her untimely end.

In the course of time and upheaval, this branch of the Fitzpatricks were expelled from Ossory, and settled down in the district of O'More where a descendant erected a mansion. He was sceptical about the appearances of the Banshee, despite the stories told by his old retainer, who maintained she had heard the Banshee the night his father had died in London. As the years rolled on, and no Banshee was heard, he was convinced it was only superstition.

At length his favourite daughter fell suddenly ill, and at midnight he set off in his coach to fetch a doctor. On the way back, with the physician beside him, he heard a sad and solemn cry coming from the direction of the well, and thinking it was a trick by someone to mock him, on his arrival home he got his pistols and hurried back to the place. Looking through the trees he saw a female figure dressed in white sitting on the bank, uttering a melancholy cry.

Still believing it was a hoax, he aimed his pistol at the figure and fired. A scream of superhuman force and horror that nearly froze his blood burst upon him. As he turned to fly, the figure of the Banshee, all covered in blood, crossed his path, and continued, at intervals to intercept him as he ran. When he reached home, he dashed into his daughter's room and as he did, the sick girl cried out, 'See, see! oh, see that beautiful lady all covered in blood!'

'Where, oh! where?' demanded the father.

'In the window,' replied the poor creature. 'Oh, no, she's gone.'

From that moment the patient got worse, and died in the afternoon of the following day. That evening, as the sun went down, the afflicted father was pacing up and down one of the walks in his garden, when he heard the sound of a coach and horses coming up the avenue to the house.

Looking over a hedge, he saw six black headless horses, driven by a headless coachman, drawing a hearse, which stopped before his hall door. A coffin was taken out and placed at the top of the steps leading to the entrance, and suddenly the figure of the Banshee mounted upon the pall, and the hearse drove away. Recovering from the shock, the agitated man rushed into the house, to find the body of his beloved daughter, lying on her bed with members of his family around it.

When he told his wife what he had seen, she said 'That hearse follows my father's family. I saw it myself when one of my uncles died, and it is quite as natural as the Banshee.'

'But look,' said Fitzpatrick, 'there she is outside the window, bloody and vindictive-looking as when I shot her! She recedes, she's gone! Heaven defend me from her wrath, for I'm sure she bore me evil.'

His apprehensions were too true, the next day another of his daughters died suddenly. Any night he went out walking afterwards, the terrifying figure of the Banshee crossed his path, whether he rode or walked, alone or in company. At length, in the hope of avoiding her he went over to live in England, where he died soon after.

Strangely enough, after Fitzpatrick's night of terror, the Banshee of the well was never heard again, and the events were almost forgotten, but there are still a few old people who talk about them up to the present day.

How the Bellews got their Banshee

The stronghold of the Bellews at Gullen, Castletown, Co. Louth, commanded the pass from Dublin to Dundalk. From the battlements of the castle there was a fine view of Dundalk and its bay, closed in by Slieve Gullen and the Carlingford Mountains. Originally of Norman race, the Bellews accompanied William the Conqueror into England, and Strongbow into Ireland. They obtained large grants of land in the counties of Meath and Louth, and the fine estate of Mount Bellew in Co. Galway.

In the seventeenth century the area of Castletown was under the mastery of a knight of ancient lineage named Sir Patrick Bellew. He was handsome with winning manners, frank and joyous in disposition, but much attracted to bachelors' revelries. He preferred to hear the glasses clink on the board around which sat a score of jovial companions, with whom he hunted all day, to drinking mead with ladies. He also liked the colour of ruby wine better than ruby lips or peachy cheeks. To the disappointment of all the mothers of marriageable daughters in and around Dundalk, he remained obstinately 'single', when he ought to have indulged in the luxury of a wife.

It happened one day that the chase was longer and harder than usual. The hounds found a fleet doe near Lough Dagneach, and soon the glens on Slieve Gullen reverberated with the cries of the tuneful pack. Sir Patrick blew his bugle and shouted in excitement, as he urged the dogs in pursuit. A first-class horseman, he took all the fences in his way with ease, but the pace soon told upon his gallant horse, carrying fifteen stone over rough ground at racing speed.

The sun was high overhead when the hunt began, and already the declining beams were gilding the western hills, and the broad moon looking down on the flagging chase. All the field had disappeared, save Sir Patrick, who with three of his staunchest hounds, kept up the pursuit. Suddenly he missed both deer and hounds. A dark mound lay before him and he drew a breath. He dismounted, threw the reins of his jaded and foaming horse on the nearest bush, and climbed the moat to see where the hounds had gone. As he did so, the restless horse freed the rein from the bush, and instinctively made his way at leisure home to his stable. The grooms and servants at the castle, amazed and frightened on seeing the riderless horse, went out in search of their lord, and following the hoof-tracks reached the high moat of Dundalgan.

The silvery light of the full moon revealed a beautiful panorama – below stood the tall and stately towers of Cathlomer, near it the ivy-clad church and the houses of the hamlet; seaward lay Dundalk, with the distant sea shimmering with light. The servants made their way to the summit, searching everywhere. When they reached the top, there, stretched on the level surface was the body of Sir Patrick Bellew. He was barely breathing, and his limbs were rigid and icy cold. They bore him quickly back to the castle where they began to revive him in front of the huge hall fire. Eventually he gave a deep sigh, as if he regretted leaving some beloved object, and opening his eyes stared wildly around. Soon realising where he was, he told the servants to lay him on a couch and leave him. He then sank into deep and peaceful sleep.

Now we may tell what happened when Sir Patrick reached the top of the moat. Feeling worn out from the steep ascent he sat down to rest. Whether he fell asleep or not he couldn't tell, but suddenly, approaching him, he saw a beautiful lady in regal robes, with a diadem blazing with jewels on her head. She bent over him, and taking him by the hand, said in a lovely soft voice – 'My dear Sir Patrick, I perceive I have tired you very much.'

'Yes, your majesty,' replied Sir Patrick, 'I never had the honour of seeing you before this.'

'Indeed you did,' she answered laughing. 'I am the lily-white doe you chased from Slieve Gullen, and as you seem both tired and hungry, the best atonement

I can make is to procure you refreshment and repose. Follow me.'

Fascinated by her charms and engaging conversation, Sir Patrick allowed her to conduct him to the centre of the moat, where they found a trap-door open, and a flight of steps, which they went down. It led to a spacious hall, brilliantly lighted, and filled with a glittering throng – evidently the lords and ladies of the queen's court, for as she appeared they all drew aside and opened a passage through which she conducted Sir Patrick to a canopy of state at the end of the hall. When they sat down delicious music struck up, dancing was resumed, and a retinue of servants bore dainty dishes to the throne. Having eaten heartily with wines of exquisite flavour, the queen asked Sir Patrick if he would like to dance.

'With you for my partner, willingly,' he replied, and soon the well-watched couple were whirling away to the great admiration of the courtiers. Having danced until both were out of breath, Sir Patrick sank beside the beautiful queen upon a couch of downy softness and told her 'she was the best partner he ever had, or could have.'

'I am glad to hear you say so, my dear Sir Patrick,' she said, 'for I mean to have you as my partner for more than a dance. I expect you'll marry me.'

'It's not for the want of encouragement,' he thought, 'it's rather hard that above or below, I can't escape the girls.'

'May I have the honour of knowing who you are, your subjects, and to what royal family you belong, you charming and beautiful creature?' he said in his most insinuating tone.

'My name is Aine,' she replied in her low, sweet voice. 'I am sister of Milncruadh, the Callach Biovar of Lough Dagneach of Slieve Gullen. I am Queen of Flothinis, in the bay of Dundalk, as is well-known to the natives of Dunany.'

'That's enough,' responded Sir Patrick, 'a respectable connection and no mistake. I'm your man.'

'Then the sooner we're made happy the better,' she whispered, and summoned her Prime Minister to make all the arrangements.

It was at this stage that Sir Patrick suddenly found himself forced to undergo the cold realities of this world. For some time he was an altered man, reserved and unhappy, but as months wore on, he fell back into his old habits, and became as ardent a lover of the banquet and the chase as before.

It happened by a strange coincidence, that nine months from the day he chased the white doe from Slieve Gullen, he again had the same game afoot, and lost the deer once more at the moat of Dundalgan. Again he dismounted and climbed the height, and no sooner had he reached the summit than he sank into what appeared to be a slumber. Again the lovely queen approached, but this time carried something wrapped up in her arms. When she drew near, Sir Patrick saw the form of a newly-born baby, carefully covered up. 'Here,' she said, laying tenderly in his arms the fragile burden – 'Take your daughter, Maire Ruadh Bellew. Never cease to treat her as your child, but observe this caution – for twelve months and a day from this, sun or moon must not light on her. If only one ray gleams through the room in which you place her, your child is no longer on earth.'

Then she disappeared, and Sir Patrick heard the shrill cry of a child in his ear. He started and found himself in darkness, with barely light enough to see he was on the summit of the fort of Dundalgan, that his castle was looming below, and that the cry he heard came from a living child, the tiny babe nestling in his arms.

The wonder of his household seeing him return thus laden may be imagined. He quickly procured the services of a trustworthy young mother, who having recently lost an infant, undertook to nurse her tender charge in rooms lit by waxen tapers for a year and a day. Nothwithstanding this, Maire Ruadh Bellew grew in strength and ever increasing beauty.

Sir Patrick was very fond of her. He would spend hours in her nursery dangling her on his knee, watching her as she played, the lovely tresses of her golden coloured hair, and laying out plans for her education befitting the heiress of Castletown Bellew. All went well for a year, but on the morning of the following day Sir Patrick got a message that his presence was required in Dublin by the Lord Deputy, who wanted his advice on state affairs. Bidding the nurse be careful of her charge, on this, the day which was to terminate her close confinement, Sir Patrick set off for Dublin.

Shortly after he left a most impressive carriage drove into the principal entrance to Castletown Bellew. The carriage, with a lady inside, blazed with armorial bearings, and the winkers and trappings of the eight cream-coloured horses were mounted in gold. There were eight out-riders in scarlet liveries, and the impression on the household of Castletown, when the cortege drew up, was that the Queen of England had arrived there in state. Sir Patrick had left positive orders that no one should be admitted under any circumstances whatever, so when the grooms and footmen were told that their lady would not be admitted into the castle, they began knocking loudly on the door. But it was in vain. The door was kept shut. Still the knocking continued, and eventually became so alarmingly loud that the nurse drew aside one of the shutters to learn the cause of the uproar. A ray of sunlight fell upon the cradle in which slept Maire Ruadh Bellew. It was soon empty. A hand swiftly descended upon the unconscious child and bore her through the opening of the window. The beautiful lady leaning out of the coach, received the child in her arms, and rapidly the horses bore Maire Ruadh Bellew away.

The Lord Deputy had not summoned Sir Patrick to the Council. On his return he was almost insane at finding himself childless. He soon left the country, and no one knew where he spent the rest of his life, but ever since the Banshee of the family is Maire Ruadh Bellew.

When a spirit has fled, she wails the dead
All about her there's no more to be said.

Farewell to an Eminent Harper

by Thomas Crofton Croker

Rev. Charles Bunworth was Rector of Buttevant in Co. Cork in the middle of the eighteenth century. He was a man of unaffected piety, of sound learning, pure in heart and benevolent in intention. By the rich he was respected, and by the poor beloved. He even looked after those of a different creed in matters of difficulty, and times of distress, giving the advice and assistance that a father could afford to his children. He was the friend and benefactor of the surrounding countryside, and from the nearby town of Newmarket, both Curran and Yelverton came to him for advice and instruction before they went on to study at Trinity College in Dublin. Young, intelligent and inexperienced, these eminent men received from him, in addition to the advice they sought, financial aid, and their brilliant careers later justified the discrimination of the giver.

But what extended the fame of Mr Bunworth far beyond the limits of the parishes beyond his own, was his performance on the Irish harp, and his hospitality to the poor harpers who travelled from house to house throughout the country. Grateful to their patron, these itinerant minstrels sang his praises to the accompanying tingle of their instruments, invoking blessings on his head, and in their verses praising the charms of his two daughters, Elizabeth and Mary. At the time of his death, no less than fifteen harps were found in the loft of his granary, given to him by the last members of a race that had ceased to exist. It is regretted that after his death these harps were broken up and used as firewood by an ignorant relation left in charge of the house.

The circumstances attending the death of Mr Bunworth may be doubted by some, but there were many credible witnesses to declare their authenticity. About a week previous to his demise, a noise was heard at the hall-door, resembling the shearing of sheep, but at the time no particular attention was paid to it. It was near 11 o'clock that same night, when Kavanagh the herdsman returned from Mallow, where he had been sent in the afternoon for some medicine, and was observed by one of the Miss Bunworths, to whom he delivered the package, to be much agitated. At this time her father was not considered to be in much danger.

'What is the matter?' she asked him, but the poor fellow only stammered – 'The Master, Miss, the Master – he is going from us,' and overcome with grief he burst into tears.

Miss Bunworth, a woman of strong nerve, enquired if he had heard anything in Mallow that made him suppose that her father was worse.

'No,' said Kavanagh, 'it was not in Mallow.'

'Kavanagh,' said Miss Bunworth in the superior manner for which she was noted, 'I'm afraid you have been drinking, which I did not expect you to be doing at a time like this, when it should be your duty to stay sober – what would we have done if you had broken the bottle, or lost it, as the doctor said that it was important that your master should take it tonight. I will speak further to you in the morning, when you are in a more fit state to know what I am saying.'

Kavanagh looked at her stupidly, which did not remove the impression of his being drunk, as his eyes appeared heavy and dull after his weeping – but his voice was not one of an intoxicated person.

'Miss,' he said, 'as I hope to receive mercy hereafter, neither bite nor sup has passed my lips since I left the house but the Master – '

'Speak softly,' said Miss Bunworth. 'He's asleep, and as well as can be expected.'

'Thank God for that,' said Kavanagh, 'but oh! Miss, he is going from us surely – we're going to lose the Master,' and he wrung his hands.

'What is it you mean, Kavanagh?' asked Miss Bunworth.

'Is it mean?' said Kavanagh. 'The Banshee has come for him, Miss – and 'tis not I alone would have heard her.'

'That's an idle superstition,' said Miss Bunworth.

'Maybe so,' replied Kavanagh, 'but as I came through the glen of Ballybeg, she was along with me, keening and screeching and clapping her hands, by my side every step of the way, with her long white hair falling about her shoulders, and I could hear her repeat the Master's name over and over again, as plain as I ever heard it. When I came to the old abbey, she parted from me, and turned into the pigeon-field next to the burying ground, and folded her cloak around her; she sat down under the tree that was struck by lightning, and began keening so bitterly, that it pierced me to the heart.'

Miss Bunworth had listened intently and when he finished said, 'Kavanagh, my father is, I believe, on the mend, and I expect him to be up soon, and able to convince you that this is all your own fancy, but I warn you not to mention what you have just told me, for there is no point in frightening your fellow-servants with your tale.'

However, over the next few days, Mr Bunworth gradually declined, but nothing in particular occurred until the night previous to his death. That night, both his daughters, exhausted from continued attendance and watching, were prevailed upon to seek some repose, and an elderly lady, a near relative and friend of the family, sat by the bedside of their father. The old gentleman lay in the parlour, where he had been removed at his own request, hoping the change would give him some relief, and the head of his bed was placed close to the window. In a room adjoining sat some male friends, and as usual on such occasions of illness, many of the followers of the family had assembled in the kitchen.

The night was peaceful, with the moon shining, and nothing broke the silence of the melancholy watch, when the little party in the room adjoining the parlour, the door of which stood open, were suddenly aroused by a sound at the window near the bed: a rose-tree grew outside, almost touching the glass, and this was forced aside with some noise, and a low moaning was heard, accompanied by clapping of hands, as of a female in deep affliction. It seemed as if the sound came from a person holding her mouth close to the window.

Alarmed, the lady at the bedside ran into the adjoining room, and asked the gentlemen if they had heard the Banshee? Sceptical of supernatural matters, two of them arose hastily and went out to discover the source of the sounds, which they had also distinctly heard. They walked all around the house, examining every spot of ground, particularly near the window, from where the voice emanated. Their search was in vain, they heard nothing, and outside all was silent. They continued searching around the garden, and even the road outside, but all to no avail. When they returned to the house, to their amazement, they learned that during their absence those indoors had heard the moaning and clapping even louder than before, and as soon as the two men closed the door of the room, they themselves heard the same mournful sounds again. Hour by hour, the sick man became worse, and with the first glimpse of morning, Mr Bunworth expired.

(The writer claimed that this was a true story, and that the harp made for Mr Bunworth by Kelly was still in the possession of the family in the early nineteenth century – in the home of his grand-daughter, Miss Dillon of Blackrock near Cork.)

Selections from a Ghostly Feature

During the winter months from 1962 to 1979 I compiled a weekly feature on ghosts in the Dublin *Evening Herald*, in which readers submitted their supernatural experiences. There were many stories about the Banshee, and here are some of the best ones.

(i) Little Woman in London

An exile living in London wrote: 'Years ago my family back in Ireland often talked about the Banshee, a little woman who came at midnight and screamed the house down and filled everyone with gloom and despair. What truth was in those stories I cannot tell, for like most young people I thought they were just a lot of old-hat, and were only made up to frighten us to go asleep, but now I am not so sure!

'I live in a modern area of London, the streets are well lit and the houses are newly-built, and to think of there being ghosts anywhere about would cause a roar of laughter from the folk who live here. They would look upon it as Irish superstition. One night in December, my wife and I retired just after midnight. Soon we were both fast asleep, not a sound, not even the wind caused either of us to awaken. . . the night was as still as the grave. But suddenly we were both awakened by a terrible noise.

'Scream after scream came from the courtyard below our window – we both got up and rushed to look outside, expecting to see some person being murdered! But the courtyard was empty, nothing moved, not even a stray cat, but the screaming continued right under the window. The next day we asked the neighbours if they had heard anything during the night, but the result was negative. The following night we heard the terrible screaming again. Three awful unearthly wails, then silence as before. Two days later my wife got a telegram telling her that her father had died in Ireland. We both went home for the funeral, and afterwards talking with the wife's people, one person remarked on the terrible screams she had heard on the same night my wife and myself had heard them in London. We were told that the Banshee followed the Murphy family (my wife's maiden name). I little thought that the Banshee wail would have reached as far as such an unbelieving city as London!'

(ii) Experience in Co. Kildare

A Dublin resident wrote: 'In July 1912 I was working cutting down timber in a large wood on the Moorefield estate just outside Newbridge, Co. Kildare. At that time there was a large quantity of timber on the estate, and the agents wanted the land cleared for building purposes. We had a portable saw mill in one of the woods, and it was beside a by-road leading out to the Ballymany road on the edge of the Curragh. One man had to stay with the mill and outfit over the weekends.

'This particular time it was my turn. Opposite where we had the huts and the saws there was an old broken-down house, just across the road, about fifty feet from the hut where I was sleeping. I was told that a family lived in that old house for hundreds of years, but that they were now living in a new house just about one hundred yards away.

'I was much on the alert during the hours of darkness, as we had trouble with prowlers. This particular night I was suddenly awakened about 3 am by the sound of keening. It gradually got louder, and was like a woman or girl crying. I got up to investigate – the night was very dark – but I could see well through the huts and piles of logs. Suddenly another sound of crying started on the road opposite the old house. Something told me it was not a living woman's cry!

'I plucked up courage and went out on the old road out of the wood. I could see nothing at first, but after a few seconds a most awful keen, more like a roar, came from about ten yards in front of me. I was frozen to the ground. Then I could see plainly a small woman. She was about four feet high, and I couldn't tell whether she was sitting or standing. Her clothes seemed to be the same colour as the beech logs and her head was covered with a kind of cape. She was moving her hands up and down as she kept on wailing. I fled back to the hut. The following day I heard that Mr Kelly, the owner of the old house, had died during the night.'

(iii) Apparition in Rathmines

A Dublin lady wrote: 'When I was a child we had an old maid-servant who had been with our family for thirty years, and she often told us how she had seen and heard the Banshee, "a little red-haired woman, standing on the garden wall and crying", the night before a neighbour of ours died. We lived in Grosvenor Square, Rathmines – not a remote or lonely place – and we used to laugh at her for her superstition. Years later, however, when I was grown up, I was reading by the fire one night at about 10.30, after the family had gone to bed, when I was disturbed (in every sense of the word) by the most appalling cries and sobbing, coming from our front garden.

'I ran and opened the window, but I could see that the small garden, lit by the street lamp outside, was empty. In spite of this, coming from a spot in the centre of the garden, there arose these terrible cries, in a contralto voice, of a woman in most bitter grief. It couldn't have been a dog or cat, and as I listened tears of terror poured down my cheeks. I ran into the hallway to find that my two aunts, my uncle and my cousin had come down from their bedrooms, thinking it was I who was in trouble.

'As we stared at each other, the cries died away down the lane at the side of the house, toward Leinster Road, where a lady we all knew was seriously ill.

When we got up next morning we learned that she had died around the time we heard the wailing. I had never before or since felt such fright or horror, nor did I ever laugh again at old Margaret for being superstitious.'

(iv) Near Slieve Gullion

A woman from Kilkenny wrote: 'I remember my father, whose name was Byrne, often telling me how the Banshee followed the Byrne family, and he told me his own experience. His home and place of birth was in Co. Armagh, near the foot of Slieve Gullion.

'He was standing outside his own door on a bright moonlit night about 11 pm and looking across to his cousin's house, which lay a few fields away, he noticed a light there, and thought something must be amiss in it, as the family usually retired early. He stood there wondering if he should go over, in case they required any help, as there was only his aged uncle and aunt and their three daughters, one of whom had been unwell for years.

'Then he heard a long wailing cry. The cry seemed to go round and round one of the fields between his house and the house of his cousins. Still he stood there, not daring to move while the wailing continued. He said afterwards that it was a long, heartbreaking cry which went on all through the night.

'"Surely," he thought, "'tis the Banshee: some of the Byrnes, or the Haggarts, or the Hanaways, must be going to die, as they are all connections of the Byrnes and that for certain is the Banshee." Next morning a messenger brought the sad news to his house that his cousin Mary, the delicate girl, had died early that morning.

'There were other similar incidents relating to the Banshee which he often told to me, and certainly from his sincere revelations it could not have been imagination.'

(v) Residents were Terrified

Over seventy years ago reports of a Banshee terrified residents in the Sandyford area of Co. Dublin, and in this connection the following tale came from my friend the late Denis Brennan, actor and well-known radio personality: 'I was born and spent most of my boyhood in the village of Sandyford, and I heard a lot of local lore from my mother and my late grandmother. This incident came from my grandmother to my mother, and so to me.

'My grandmother, a Mrs Haydon (who will be well remembered by the older inhabitants) knew a family by the name of Pielow who owned a quite extensive farm across the road from her house. The portion of this farm near the house known as "the haggard" where the hay was stored when drawn in, was, reputedly, a great haunt of our "Sandyford Banshee". My grandmother reported many a sleepless night as a result of her caterwauling.

'Mr Pielow was a practical man. Such disturbances were not to be tolerated! One night, having been awakened from his peaceful slumbers by this howling, the good gentleman lost his temper. He went to the stable, took down a large horsewhip, marched to "the haggard", dressed in pants pulled up about his nightshirt, and on being confronted by "the Banshee", proceeded to attempt to belabour her with the whip.

'After the first stoke, the "Banshee" screamed loudly, and flung a comb, with which she had been combing her hair, at him. He staggered back, but succeeded in whipping the little woman out of the haggard. Then feeling quite satisfied that he had rid himself of a human nuisance he returned to his bed. He never left it again alive! He took ill that night, and died soon after.'

*(vi) A Dreadful Experience**

Aiden Grennell came down to the theatre one evening in a terrible state. He said he had had a dreadful experience. This was before he was married, when he was living in digs in Lower Mount Street, Dublin.

In his bedroom there were two beds, one of which was usually empty. After the evening show he found that the landlady had let the other bed to someone else. She was entitled to, and Aiden could make no complaint. The man was asleep anyway, so there was nothing to do but go to bed himself.

At three o'clock in the morning the stranger in the other bed began to groan. Tragic dying groans, groans to put the heart across you. Aiden switched on the light to see what could be done. As he looked at the sleeping man moaning convulsively a shadow began to form over this stranger's diaphragm and gradually grew larger until it turned into an old woman with grey straggling locks who muttered and wept woefully, wringing her hands. She gradually moved behind the bed and disappeared into the shadows by the wardrobe. Needless to say Aiden stayed under the bed-clothes shivering and shaking for the rest of the night.

He came down to the theatre that evening in quite

* 'A Dreadful Experience' and 'On the Shores of Lough Derg' were told to me by the well-known actor, Christopher Casson.

a state and we told him to throw Holy Water at the stranger, as that might keep him quiet or even save him from whatever was troubling him. We hadn't any to give him that evening so Aiden had to face another night without it.

Punctual to the minute at three o'clock the groans began again and the shadow started to emerge, but Aiden stayed under the bed-clothes after that.

We gave him a bottle of Holy Water and he said that he would sprinkle the man with it. As soon as the groans began Aiden jumped up and threw Holy Water over the stranger with quite a splash. All groans ceased immediately. The man's convulsions ceased and he dropped off into a child-like and calm sleep. The next night the man was moved to another room but Aiden heard him screaming in the early hours of the morning.

(vii) On the Shores of Lough Derg

At Coolbawn on the shores of Lough Derg in Co. Tipperary lived the Bruce sisters, famous for good works and officials of the St John Ambulance Brigade. They were various aunts and the mother of Tyrrell Pine, an actor at the Gate Theatre and a composer of music. Bertie Bruce, his youngest aunt, was making a fire for a picnic by the lake-shore while the others were out fishing. The fire was in an enclosed spot bounded by the lake on one side and two impassable hedges on the other.

Bertie had just turned away for a moment to collect some wood when she looked back to the fire and there was an old lady in rags leaning over it. Bertie went up to her and offered her bread, but she muttered incomprehensibly and would not take it so Bertie went back to collect more faggots. She glanced back to the fire. The old woman had totally disappeared! How had she gone with no one seeing her? How had she got there? There was no way. And later the others who were out in the boat said they had seen no one.

It turned out afterwards that a member of the family had died at that moment in a house nearby. They were known to be followed by a Banshee. . .

From Generation to Generation

Béaloideas, the journal of the Department of Irish Folklore, University College, Dublin has preserved for posterity hundreds of stories about the Banshee from all parts of Ireland. Here is a selection from them.

Folklore collector Seán Ó Flannagain heard this one from a Co. Galway farmer Seamus Ó Cealla of Killeen Beagh in 1937:

'I used to hear my father saying that there was an old man of the Regans who lived here in Killeen a good many years ago. There were no candles or lamps in them times, but 'twas how everyone used to go to the bog and root up a good thick block of bog deal timber and bring it home with him. He'd get his hatchet then and split that block up into sliseogs, which were dipped into tallow that they'd get out of the cattle or sheep they'd kill, and then whenever they'd want a light they used one of them, and some-one would hold them in his hand or maybe they'd put it standing in the middle of a heap of potatoes while they'd be eating them for supper. The sliseogs they burned that way were called caisnins. They didn't have them burning all night, but used them only while they'd be putting down a pot, or taking up a pot, or if they were looking for something around the house. For the rest of the time they'd sit around the fire telling stories – the light of the turf fire was enough for them.

'Well, this ould man of the Regans – he had a big stump of bog like that beyant in Carrachan Bog, just at the foot of the mountain, or in the mountain, as you might say. He had the stump rooted up, and thrown on the bank ready to bring home, and as night had fallen he made over across towards Carrachan, near where a stream runs down. Suddenly, didn't he hear the sound of beetling (washing clothes) going on. He was a kind of harum-scarum of a young man then, and he wasn't afraid of man or devil. He made across to where the sound came from, and sure enough he saw her there. She had a beetle in one hand and a lovely rack (comb) in another. He stepped lightly up behind her, snapped the rack out of her hand and made one leap for the other bank and away with him home, as fast as he could.

'Away with the Banshee after him, and every scream out of her worse than another. She flung the beetle after him, and I suppose 'twas God that saved him, or that he didn't give her the power to hit him, but anyway the beetle went whistling past his poll, and if it hit him he was a dead man. But Regan was a great runner and always managed to keep ahead of her. She took up the beetle and threw it again, missing him for the second time. Again she took it up, when Regan was just turning in home at his own gable-end. He had just landed inside his own door when the beetle struck the gable-end and shook the house from top to bottom. He bolted the door and secured it from the inside with the wooden plank they used to have in them days to secure the door in the time of a storm.

'The family were all sitting down inside, and wasn't the heart put across them when they heard the scream outside the door. She told them in Irish to throw out the rack to her, or she'd knock down the house. Regan got up and fetched a spade, and he put the rack on the top of it, and holding it by the handle pushed the rack out under the door to her. Half the iron of the spade was outside the door and the other half inside. She caught the rack and half of the iron that was outside, and brought the rack and half the spade with her. When they pulled in the spade again wasn't half of it gone! Next morning when they got up and went outside didn't they find the gable-end of the house split in two even halves from thatch to ground, and any day you go over to see Regan's ould ruin you'll see the gable-end split in two even halves and that's how it happened.'

In another story, Seamus Ó Cealla told how the ghostly messenger is also supposed to leave the imprint of her fingers, not only on the comb she throws away, but on the head or face of anyone unfortunate enough to encounter her.

'Thomas Harte's uncle was coming home from his cuaird this night, it was bright and the moon was high in the sky. Outside his house was a green flag, and as he was coming near it didn't he see a woman standing on it. He thought it was a neighbour that was there, and it was how she was trying to knock a start out of him. Over he goes and claps his hand on her shoulder. The very minute he did – God bless us and save us all and may everyone be well where it is told – she raised her hand and caught him by the crown of the head and lifted him clear off the road. And she hit him down against the ground again, but she did not kill him. He got a terrible fright. And may God bless and save us all, when he got up in the morning the print of her five fngers was on the top of his head and his hair had turned as white as the snow from the dent of the fright.'

(i) Sequel to Bog Drowning

Thomas Reilly was returning home from a spree in a neighbour's house and his way lay through a field, and at the bottom of the field there was a small piece of bog. Some years before that the daughter of a neighbouring farmer was accidentally drowned in a bog-hole in this bog when she was on her way home from a dance. She was wearing a white dress, and after her death there were a lot of stories about people having seen a white woman roaming over the bog at night. Now, as Thomas Reilly came into the field beside the bog he saw a white woman coming towards him. Thinking it was a local woman, and as he had some drink taken, he attempted to catch hold of her. She stepped back and said: 'Curse you and your future generations.' She then gave him a slap of her hand on the right side of his face. Next morning his wife found him unconscious in the field, his head and face twisted round from the right. His head was so twisted that his face was almost where the back of his head should be. The doctor could do nothing for him, and he died after a few months; but before he died he told people what had happened to him. His son, Michael, lived on in the place, and later he got married. He had four children. The two eldest girls were feeble-minded. The next child was a son and he was an idiot. At the time he was fifty years old,

Michael Reilly took cancer and it ate away the right side of his head and face before he died. None of his children got married.

(ii) Two Tales from Kerry

There was a man about thirty-one years old dying in my home town, Kilmalkepar, and I was with his people consoling them around the bedside. They asked me to go and call on two sisters, their first cousins, to ask them to come down to see the man who was dying. When I arrived, a young boy of the house, the brother of the man who was dying, gave me a basket, and asked me to bring in turf from the bin outside. I went out and was putting the turf in the kish, when the Banshee came up to me. I looked at her, and she gave a wail and frightened me. It was the most terrifying cry I ever heard, before or since. She went around the house, and then stood outside the kitchen door and gave another wail, and again outside the window of the room where the man lay dying. He raised his head from the pillow, poor man, and said – 'That is the woman of my people.' He died a few hours later at 2 o'clock in the morning.

There was a family named Hussey in Dingle long ago, and every time one of them died the Banshee was heard going around the town and crying. There was a time when one of them was dying, and in the middle of the night the Banshee started wailing. At that time John Street was full of little houses, and when the people inside heard her, they became very frightened. The Banshee realised this. She stopped crying and said loudly, so as they could hear:

> Listen, listen you hoarding traders,
> You are not in danger, but they have need to fear
> A Banshee never keened for your kind.

She then started crying again, and the next day they heard that one of the Husseys was dead.

(The lines of poetry are from a poem by Piaras Feiriteir written on the occasion of the death of a friend in 1642)

(iii) The Woman who Hopped like a Magpie

The following stories were told to Miss L. McManus of Killeaden, Co. Mayo in 1902, and later appeared in the journal *Folklore.* The narrator was an engineer in the Congested Districts Board, a Mayoman of Scots-Gaelic descent:

'Some friends had been spending the day at our place, and my brother drove them home at night. He brought a sheepdog with him. It was about 12 o'clock as he was coming back between Foxford and Kiltebern Wood, at a place where the old whitethorn tree grows by the side of the road. He saw a woman jump out from beneath this tree. It was about twenty yards in front of the car. He wondered who the woman was, and said to himself, "I wonder if she is one of the Clarkes?" (a family who lived in a cottage by the side of the road further on).

'He spoke to the dog and told it to follow the woman. But instead of obeying, it whined and ran under the car, and then tried to jump up by my brother's side. He noticed that the woman ran in a peculiar way, hopping like a magpie, instead of running like a human being. He determined to overtake her, and set the horse into a smart trot, but she went in front. Being anxious to catch up with her before she reached the house, he set the horse into a gallop, but she still went ahead. When she got to the cottage, she went by, with a hood on her head, and he could see her feet clearly in the moonlight. She went on before him until she came to a sandpit on the left-hand side of the road where there is a well. She went in there, and as he drove past he heard a terrible yell.

'My brother was on horseback one night on the same road, and at about the same hour. The mare he rode was accustomed to get a drink of water at a small stream which flows underneath the road. On coming to the stream she turned in at the accustomed spot, and while she was drinking he heard a cry, as if a number of women were mourning the dead. At the same moment, he felt the mare start beneath him, and flinging up her head, she looked around. He was about a hundred yards from the tree where he had seen the woman. He said to himself, "I wonder who is dead in Shraheens", a village on the side of the mountain from which the cry came, and was surprised he had not heard of the death. For a time then, he thought nothing more of the cry, though he heard it continuously, and it seemed to be drawing nearer. He was a mile from Kiltebern Wood when he first heard it, and it went on, just like women keening, until he reached the wood. It appeared to proceed across the hill, coming towards him on the left. He now began to wonder if it were possible that anyone was to be buried at such an unusual hour. There was an old church yard on his right, about a mile off, across the Moy. He tried to bring the mare to a walk in order to listen better to the sound, but she wouldn't slow down, and broke into a fast trot. By this time, he could hear the cry very distinctly, just like a lot of women at a wake.

'As he rode by the wood he heard movements among the trees, and sounds as if sticks were being broken under the tread of feet. When near the middle of the wood, the cry came so close that he expected to see the funeral procession leave the wood and cross the road before him. At that point the mare stopped, and refused to go on. The cry now seemed to come from the dyke. He determined to find out what was there and dismounted, putting the reins around his arm as the mare became restless. He then went close to the dyke, and felt the bottom with the ash-plant he carried as a whip, but found no one. He sprang into the saddle and cried out – "If the devil from hell is before me, I'll go through." At the same time he thought every vein in his body was like a rope. Not that he felt afraid, but just ready to fight anything. He struck the mare several times, and at last she made a spring, as if jumping a high wall, and galloped on. Immediately after she had leaped, the cry passed over the road behind him, and then he felt afraid – not very much, and rode away fast. The mare was in a terrible state, all white with foam when he got home.'

'Mr MacC– also told me this story – One night his father and a servant were returning from Ballina with two carts. Each man led his horse, and the servant's cart was first. There was a distance of three yards or so between the carts. They came to a part of the road where the country was open and bare on both sides. One wheel of the first cart appeared to go over something, and Mr MacC– heard a scream close to his feet like the cry of a peacock. He at once stopped, and held the lantern he carried over the spot, but only saw the road. He then called to his servant, but the latter went on as if he had not heard him. When he overtook the servant he asked him if he had not heard the scream. "I heard the cry well enough," the man said "but if you had seen what I saw, you wouldn't have come back. There was a little man on the road running before the horse, and by the side of the wheel, and grinning up at me. He ran back by the wheel, and then I heard the scream." This servant also said that twice on going along the road at night, a woman had jumped into the cart, and ridden in it for some distance, and that while she was sitting in it, the cart became so heavy that the horse could scarcely drag the load. She would sit still and silent, and though he dared not fully look at her, he could see her by sidelong glances. Then, having kept him company for a while, she would leap off and disappear.'

(iv) The Badhb
(from Co. Waterford)

A badhb is a big tall woman dressed in white, about ten feet in height. She has hair about four feet long and she goes along clapping her hands and tearing her hair, crying out – Ochon! Ochon! And when she comes to the house, she disturbs the fowl and kills all the birds and their eggs, and very soon after that you hear that somebody is dead. About twelve years ago, one evening at half-past seven, as Kate Caher was standing at her gate, she saw a big tall woman, dressed in white and she had terrible long foxy hair, and she clapping her hands. Ochon! Ochon! she was saying. Faix! ye might say she was frightened, and she went to call out her mother, and, just when she came out, no sign of her could be seen. She was gone off like a flying fox. A cousin of hers, a young girl, died soon after in about three months.

Bibliography

The Banshee, Patricia Lysaght
Irish Ghost Stories, Patrick F. Byrne
The Bedside Book of Irish Ghost Stories, Patrick F. Byrne
Evening Herald, Ghosts Column, 1962-1979
Béaloideas Magazine
Folklore Magazine

IRISH GHOST STORIES

Patrick Byrne

There is a strong and ancient tradition of ghosts in Ireland. The country is dotted with old castles which have, or are alleged to have, sealed rooms, and while many of the tales are obvious figments of lively imaginations, there are stories which cannot be explained away. Of these, perhaps the strangest is the case of the Gormanston Foxes, when on the death of a Viscount Gormanston, groups of foxes would gather around the castle and sit there, untouched by hounds, until the obsequies were over.

This is only one of the many tales related by the author in IRISH GHOST STORIES which tells of spooky goings-on in almost every part of the country. They include *The Wizard Earl of Kildare*; the *Scanlan Lights* of Limerick; *Buttoncap* of Tyrone; Maynooth College's haunted room; *Loftus Hall* in Wexford and an account of how the poet, Francis Ledwidge appeared to his old friend in Meath.

The stories come from a great variety of sources, Many were contributed to the weekly '*Ghosts* Column' in Dublin's *Evening Hearld,* which Patrick Byrne has been compiling every winter for some years past. Some of these have come from well-known personalities. Michael MacLiammoir tells of an uncanny experience he had when an old friend kept a promise, and the Abbey actress, Máire Ní Dhomhnaill relates a weird experience that befell her in a Belfast theatrical hotel. There are special chapters on the Banshee, Historical Ghosts, Dublin Ghosts, Poltergeists and on unusual phenomena such as *The Hungry Grass*.

LEGENDS OF IRISH WITCHES AND FAIRIES

Over the years fairies have disappeared from general view because modern man is too absorbed in his own affairs and moves too fast to take the time to meet them. As the simple and sincere people are the most likely to meet the 'good people' it is always the folk and never the scholar who record their deeds. These enthralling stories are told as they were received from the storytellers with whom Kennedy was familiar.

The fairies can do anything and are as liable to do good as evil; they can raise the wind, cause a storm, ruin the crops or make them abundant, cripple a healthy man or make a lame person walk. They do ask certain courtesies, such as never draining a glass, and leaving food in their path. When they are well-treated they are very generous, but they are deadly to those who wrong them as the reader will find out in these fascinating stories.

From Patrick Kennedy's early youth (1801-1873) he felt a deep interest in stories and legends which were peculiar to Ireland. All our superstitions, and a great part of our legendary lore, have been handed down to us from our ancestors and Kennedy's dearest wish was that their memory should not fade from the minds of the people. He recorded these stories as they were told to him by the people around the fireside.